THIS BOOK BELONGS TO

_____

DEDICATION:

I DEDICATE THIS BOOK TO ALL MY STUDENTS WHO HAVE BEEN ROOTING FOR ME SINCE I HAVE STARTED THIS JOURNEY. THANK YOU FOR YOUR SUPPORT AND I APPRECIATE EVERY ONE OF YOU!

TODAY, STEVIE IS AT SCHOOL AND IT IS TIME FOR RECESS BUT IT STARTS TO RAIN.

SHE LOOKS OUT THE WINDOW AND SEES A RAINBOW APPEAR!

STEVIE IS EAGER TO ASK HER TEACHER, "MS M, I SEE A RAINBOW! WHERE DID THAT COME FROM?"

MS M GATHERS THE CLASS TOGETHER TO EXPLAIN.

SHE STARTS BY SAYING, "WELL, THE SUNLIGHT WE SEE EVERYDAY IS CALLED WHITE LIGHT."

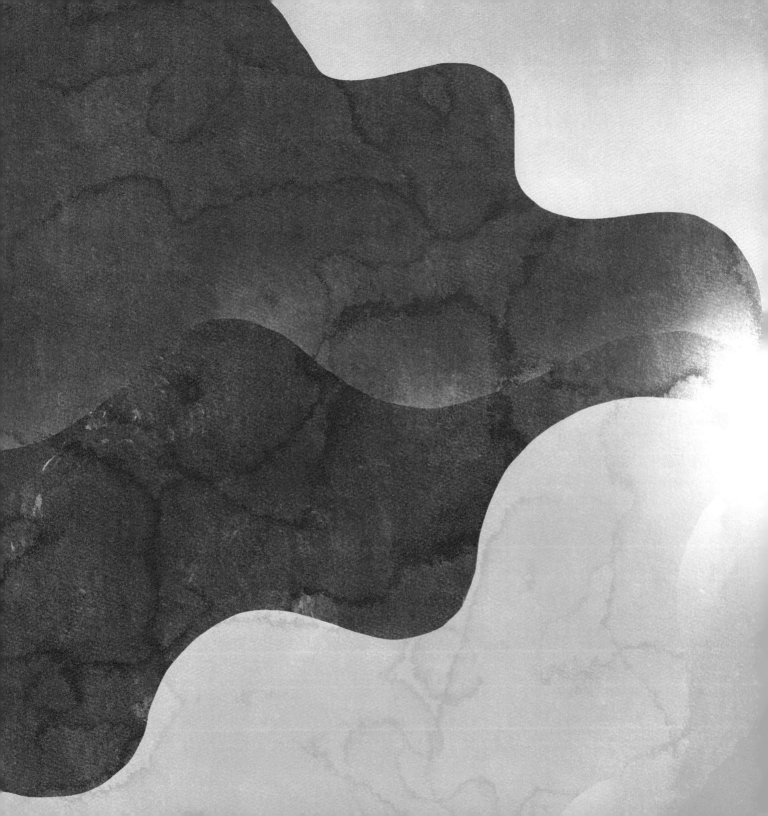

IT IS MADE BY ALL THE DIFFERENT COLORS OF THE RAINBOW BUT BLEND TOGETHER SO OUR EYES CAN ONLY SEE IT AS WHITE LIGHT.

WHITE

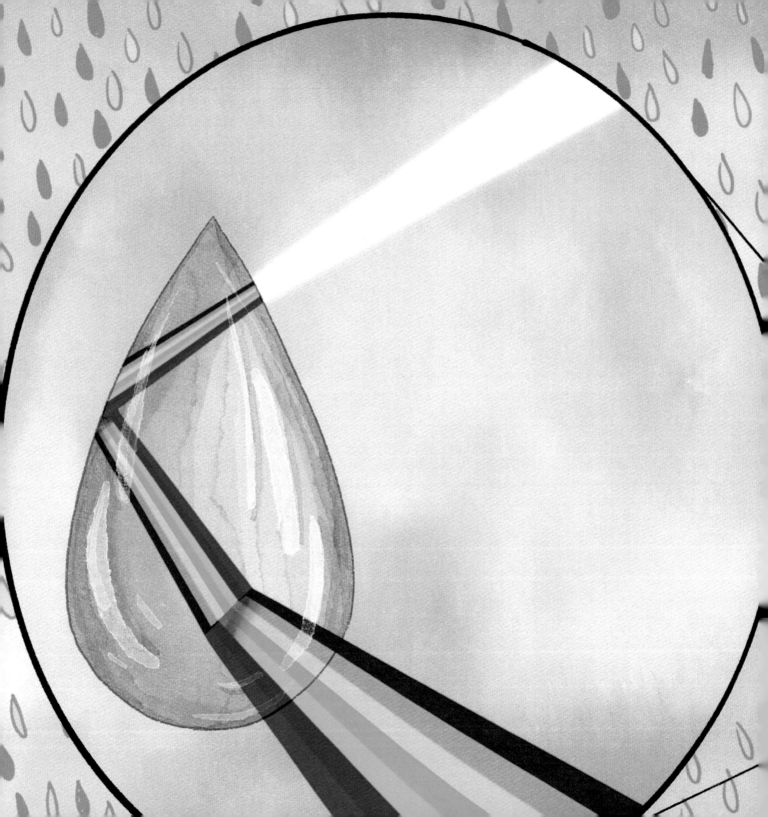

WHEN IT RAINS, THERE ARE MILLIONS OF RAINDROPS THAT FALL FROM THE SKY.
THEN THE LIGHT PASSES THROUGH THE RAINDROPS CAUSING THE COLORS IN THE WHITE LIGHT TO BEND AND SEPARATE.

MS M ASKED THE CLASS, "DID YOU KNOW THAT EACH RAINDROP MAKES ITS OWN RAINBOW?"

"THEN HOW COME WE ONLY SEE ONE RAINBOW MS M?" A STUDENT EAGERLY ASKED.

WELL, WITH ALL OF THE RAINDROPS TOGETHER AT THE SAME TIME, THE RAINBOW BECOMES BIG ENOUGH FOR US TO SEE!

"SINCE WE JUST LEARNED HOW A RAINBOW APPEARS, WHO CAN TELL ME WHAT COLORS WE SEE IN A RAINBOW?" MS M ASKED THE CLASS.

"OH MY!" MS M WAS PLEASED TO SEE ALL THE STUDENTS RAISING THEIR HANDS TO ANSWER. "LET'S SAY IT TOGETHER!"

RED

ORANGE

YELLOW

GREEN

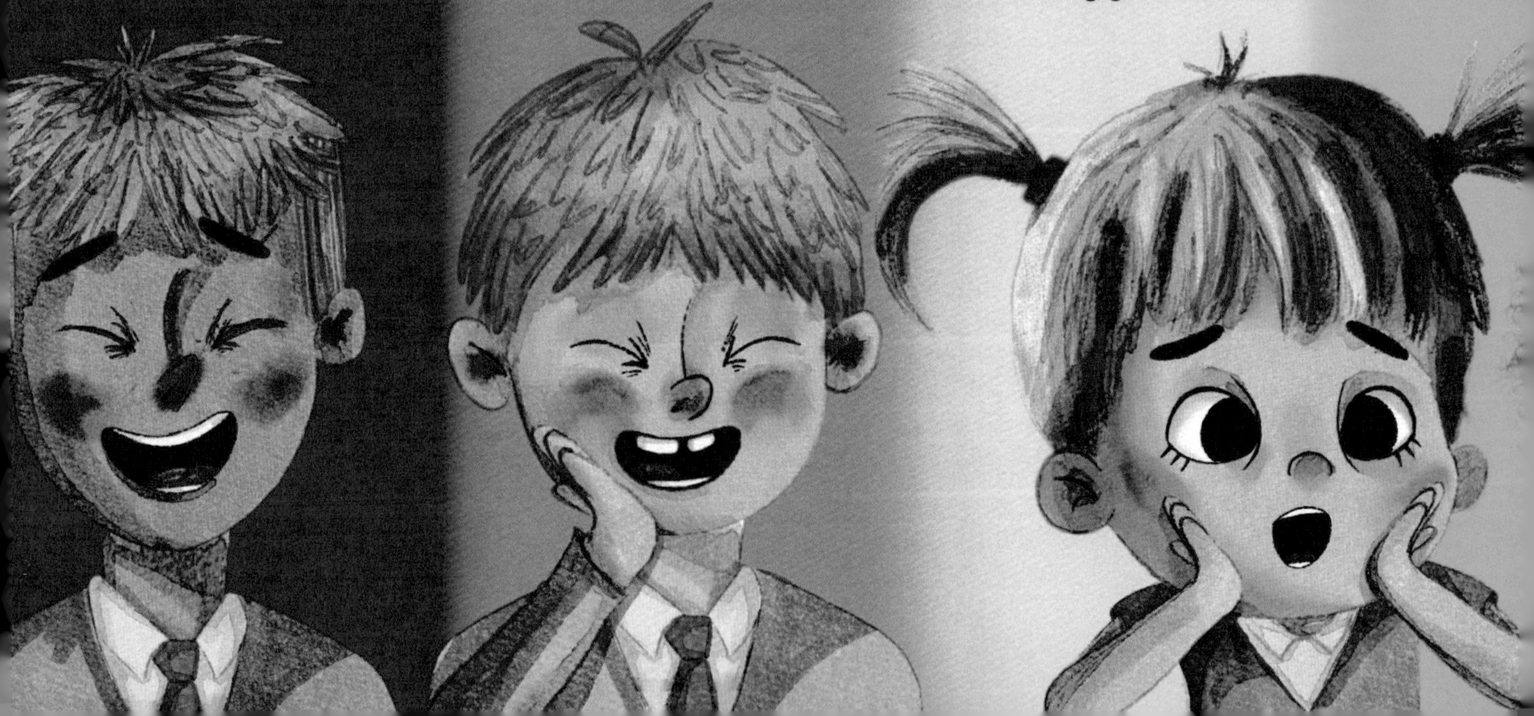

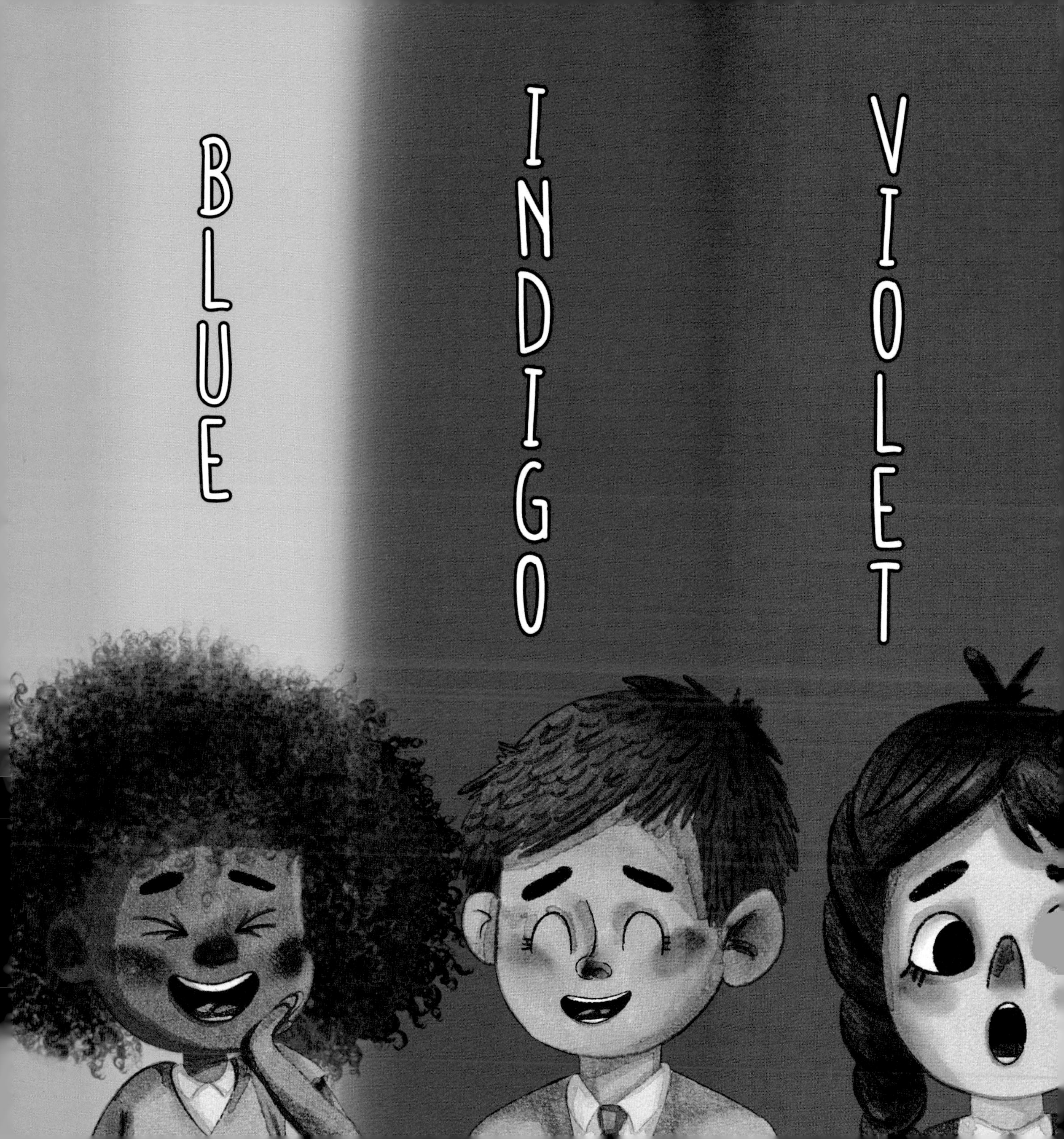
BLUE
INDIGO
VIOLET

It is really cool how rainbows appear.

Ms M s explanation made it all so clear!

What s my next question, you ll have to wait and see.

Thank you for sharing your time with me!

xoxo, stevie.

Made in the USA
Monee, IL
31 October 2024

69092608R00017